Bette
Bridges

A Beka Book® Pensacola, FL 32523-9100
an affiliate of PENSACOLA CHRISTIAN COLLEGE®

To Parents and Teachers

Children are eagerly searching for a workable sense of values. They need reading material that will give them ideals to reach for and examples to follow.

The stories in this reader have been selected from the readers of America's past and have been edited, modernized, and classroom-tested for student appeal and readability. Many character values are woven throughout the stories. Thought questions at the end of stories aid in understanding the selections.

Better Bridges
Fourth Edition

Staff Credits
Editor: Laurel Hicks
Designer: Grace Larson
Illustrators: Brian Jekel, Matthew Sample II, Becca Huber, Stan Shimmin
Cover Design: Michelle Johnson

Cataloging Data
Better Bridges / Laurel Hicks, editor.— 4th ed.
122p.: col. ill.; 24 cm. (A Beka Book reading program)
1. Readers (Primary) 2. Reading (Primary) III. Hicks, Laurel. IV. A Beka Book, Inc.
Library of Congress: PE1119 .B37 2006
Dewey System: 428.6

Contents

The Loveliest Rose in the World

Hans Christian Andersen

Once there reigned a queen, in whose garden were found the most glorious flowers at all seasons and from all the lands of the world. But more than all others she loved the roses, and she had many kinds, from the wild dog rose with its apple-scented green leaves to the most splendid, large, crimson roses. They grew against the garden walls, wound themselves around the pillars and window frames, and crept through the windows into

fragrance: a sweet odor
symbol: something that stands for something else; a sign
crimson: red
express: to show clearly, to put into words

the rooms, and all along the ceilings in the halls. And the roses were of many colors, and of every fragrance and form.

But care and sorrow dwelt in those halls. The queen lay upon a sickbed, and the doctors said she must die.

"There is still one thing that can save her," said the wisest of them. "Bring her the loveliest rose in the world, the rose that is the symbol of the purest and the brightest love. If that is held before her eyes before they close, she will not die."

Then old and young came from every side with roses, the loveliest that bloomed in each garden, but they were not of the right sort. The flower was to be plucked from the Garden of Love. But what rose in all that garden expressed the highest and purest love?

The poets sang of the loveliest rose in the world—of the love of maid and youth, and of the love of dying heroes.

"But they have not named the right flower," said the wise man. "They have not pointed out the place where it blooms in its splendor. It is not the rose that springs from the hearts of youthful lovers, though this rose will ever be fragrant in song. It is not the bloom that sprouts from the blood flowing from the breast of the hero who dies for his country, though few deaths are sweeter than his, and no rose is redder than the blood that flows then. Nor is it the wondrous flower to which man devotes many a sleepless night and much of his fresh life—the magic flower of silence."

"But I know where it blooms," said a happy mother, who came with her pretty child to the bedside of the dying queen. "I know where the loveliest rose of love may be found. It springs in the blooming cheeks of my sweet child, when, waking from sleep, he opens his eyes and smiles tenderly at me."

"Lovely is this rose, but there is one that is lovelier still," said the wise man.

"I have seen the loveliest, purest rose that blooms," said a woman. "I saw it on the cheeks of the queen. She had taken off her golden crown. And in the long, dreary night she carried her sick child in her arms. She wept, kissed him, and prayed for her child."

"Holy and wonderful is the white rose of a mother's grief," answered the wise man, "but it is not the one we seek."

"The loveliest rose in the world I saw at the altar of the Lord," said the good Bishop. "The young maidens went to the Lord's table. Roses were blushing and pale roses shining on their fresh cheeks. A young girl stood there. She looked with all the love and purity of her spirit up to Heaven. That was the expression of the highest and purest love."

"May she be blessed," said the wise man, "but not one of you has yet named the loveliest rose in the world."

Then there came into the room a child, the queen's little son.

"Mother," cried the boy, "only hear what I have read."

And the child sat by her bedside and read from the Book of Him who suffered death upon the cross to save men. “Greater love there is not.”

And a rosy glow spread over the cheeks of the queen, and her eyes gleamed, for she saw that from the leaves of the Book there bloomed the loveliest Rose in the world.

“I see it!” she said. “He who beholds this, the loveliest Rose on earth, shall never die.”

Think about it

1. What did the wise man say would cure the sick queen?
2. How many kinds of love can you name?
3. What Book did the child read to his mother?
4. What is the greatest love?
5. How could this "Rose" keep the queen from dying?

The Bible says

"But God commendeth his love toward us, in that, while we were yet sinners, Christ died for us."

—Romans 5:8

Little Brown Hands

They drive home the cows from the pasture
Up thro' the long, shady lane,
Where the quail whistles loud in the wheat
field
That is yellow with ripening grain.

They toss the hay in the meadow,
They gather the elder-bloom white;
They find where the dusky grapes purple
In the soft-tinted October light.

They wave from the tall, rocking treetops,
Where the oriole's hammock-nest swings;
And at nighttime are folded in slumber
By a song that a fond mother sings.

Those who toil bravely are strongest;
  The humble and poor become great;
And from those brown-handed children
  Shall grow mighty rulers of state.

The pen of the author and statesman,
  The noble and wise of our land—
The sword and the chisel and palette
  Shall be held in the little brown hand.

—Mary Hannah Kraut

We Thank Thee

For flowers that bloom about our feet,
For tender grass, so fresh, so sweet,
For song of bird, and hum of bee,
For all things fair we have or see,—
  Father in Heaven, we thank thee!
For blue of stream and blue of sky,
For pleasant shade of branches high,
For fragrant air and cooling breeze,
For beauty of the blooming trees,—
  Father in Heaven, we thank thee!

—Ralph Waldo Emerson

Sheltering Wings

It was extremely cold. Heavy sleds creaked continuously as they scraped over the dry, trampled snow. The signs above shop doors shrieked and groaned as they swung helplessly to and fro, and the clear, keen air seemed frozen into sharp little white needles that stabbed every living thing that must be out in it. The streets were almost forsaken in mid-afternoon. Business men hurried from shelter to shelter; every dog remained at home; not a bird was to be seen or heard. The sparrows had been forced to hide themselves in crevices and holes. The doves found protected corners and huddled together as best they could. Many birds were frozen to death.

A dozen or more doves were gathered close under the extending roof of the porch of a certain house, trying with little success

---

extremely: very
continuously: without stopping
perish: to die
meager: poor; scanty
keen: sharp
crevice: a narrow opening
radiant: shining brightly
strode: walked with long steps
revive: to come back to life

to keep warm. Some small sparrows, disturbed and driven from the cozy place they had chosen, saw the doves and came flying across to them.

"Dear doves," chirped the sparrows, "your bodies look so large and warm, won't you let us nestle near you?"

"But your coats are frosted with cold. We cannot let you come near us, for we are almost frozen now," murmured the doves, sadly.

"But we are perishing."

"So are we."

"It looks so warm near your broad wings, gentle doves. Oh, let us come. We are so little and so very, very cold."

"Come," cooed one dove at last, and a trembling little sparrow fluttered close and nestled under the broad white wing.

"Come," cooed another dove, and another little sparrow found comfort.

"Come," echoed another warm-hearted bird, and another, until at last more than half the doves were sheltering small, shivering sparrows beneath their own half-frozen wings.

"My sisters, you are very foolish," said the other doves. "You mean well, but why do you risk your own beautiful lives to give life to worthless sparrows?"

"Ah! they were so small and so very, very cold," murmured the doves. "Many of us will perish this cruel night; while we have life, let us share its meager warmth with those in bitter need."

Colder and colder grew the day. The sun went down behind clouds of soft and radiant beauty, but more fiercely swept the wind around the house where the doves and sparrows waited for death.

An hour after sunset a man came up to the house and strode across the porch. As the door of the house closed heavily behind him, a little child, watching from the window, saw something fall heavily to the porch floor.

"Oh, Papa," she cried in surprise, "a poor frozen dove has fallen on our porch."

When he stepped out to pick up the fallen dove, the father saw the others. They were no longer able to move or to utter a cry, so he brought them into a room where they might slowly revive. Soon more than half of the doves could coo gratefully and raise their stiffened wings. Then out from beneath the wings of each revived dove fluttered a living sparrow.

"Look, Papa," cried the child, "each dove that has come to life was holding a poor little sparrow close to her heart!"

They gently raised the wings of the doves that could not be revived. Not one had a sparrow beneath it.

Colder and fiercer swept the wind

without, cutting and more piercing grew the frozen needles of air, but each dove that had sheltered a frost-coated sparrow beneath her own shivering wings lived to rejoice in the glowing sunshine of the days to come.

Think about it

1. Find some sentences in the story which show how cold it was.
2. What did the sparrows ask the doves to do? Why did some of the doves refuse?
3. Why did some of the doves risk their lives to help the sparrows? Do you think they expected to be saved by their kindness?
4. Why did the kind doves live?

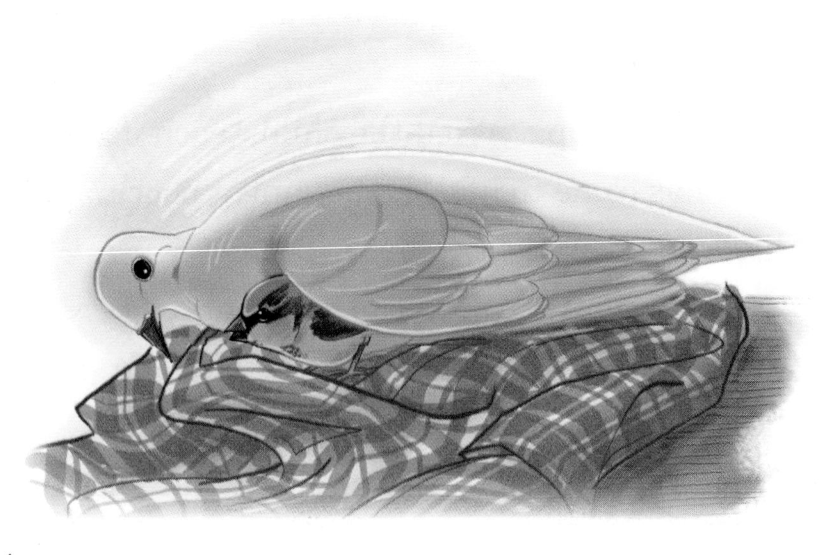

Climbing Alone

"Here, wind," cried an impatient voice, "come and help a friend in trouble, will you?"

"Certainly," replied the good-natured wind, and on arriving at the front of the cottage he found a long branch of a climbing rose striving to get loose from some bands which held it fast.

"Oh! help me, do," it said. "Help me to pull out this provoking nail that I may get free."

"Nonsense," said the wind, "that nail is there to train you properly, so that you

obstinate: stubborn
appointed: chosen, assigned
glimpse: a quick look
strive: to try hard
provoke: to make angry
delicious: enjoyable, delightful

may grow up a beautiful rose, covered with white blossoms."

"Just as if I don't know my way up the wall without any of these dreadful nails and strips of cloth," exclaimed the rose angrily.

"Well, even if you know your way—and I'm not so sure of that—I doubt that you have strength to climb without any help."

"I don't care. I don't choose to be tied," cried the impatient branch again. "And if you don't help me get loose, I'll tear away the nails myself."

"Have your own way, then," answered the wind sorrowfully, and with a little force he bent the branch forward until the nail was drawn from the wall.

A heavy shower fell that night; it bent the untied branch down to the ground.

"That delicious shower has done us all good," cried every blade of grass, every flower, every tree.

"It has not done me much good," muttered the foolish branch, as it lay

stretched on the soaking ground, splashed all over with mud.

"Well," remarked the wind, "what do you say now to a few nails and a few shreds of cloth to keep you up out of the mud?"

"I don't choose to be tied," the rose answered obstinately. "It is not at all great or grand to be tied up and nailed up. The sun isn't nailed up!"

"Why, my friend," cried the wind, "nothing that I know of in the whole wide world is more obedient than the sun. A time to rise and a time to set are given to it day by day; day by day a path is marked out for it in the heavens, and never does it stray from its appointed course."

For an instant the rose branch felt foolish.

Then it said sulkily, “Leave me alone, if you please,” and the wind went away.

“Friend,” said the branch another day to the wind, “I can sometimes get a glimpse of the rose tree high above me, and when you move by me I smell its blossoms. I haven’t a blossom or a bud upon me. I want to be beautiful and grow to the top of the wall.”

“Take my advice, then,” said the wind, “and next time a kind hand fastens you up, don’t break loose again. The rose tree would never have been anything but a straggler in the mud if it had not been for these many bonds.”

“Then lift me up, good friend, lift me up against the wall.”

“Nay, that I cannot do, but I will do what I can.” Then the wind went off, whistling loudly. It went to the drooping ash and knocked its branches against the windowpane, until the man who lived in the cottage came out with a hammer and some nails, saying,

"There must be a creeper loose somewhere." He looked about till he saw the poor rose branch trailing pitifully in the mud.

"It needs a nail terribly," he said. So he lifted it up and fastened it against the wall, and the bough clung humbly to the supports.

"Oh! what would I not give to be pure and white and sweet like the roses above me," it cried, "as I might have been if I had not been falsely proud."

The next night a gentle shower cleansed and freshened its soiled leaves.

Time went on, and lo! one summer morning there hung upon the branch a cluster of blossoms, pure white and very sweet.

"Would you not like me to draw out all those 'provoking nails'?" asked the wind in

mischief one day. But the branch only loaded her old friend with fragrance, answering playfully:

"What! and let me down into the mud again? No, thank you."

Think about it

1. Why did the rose branch want the nail pulled out?
2. Why were the nails and strips of cloth necessary?
3. What happened to the branch when he tried to grow by himself?
4. What did he see that made him want to grow tall?
5. What was the wind's advice to the branch?
6. When the man fastened the nail again, how did the branch act this time?
7. Do you think the branch wanted the nails out now? Why?

The Bible says

"The fear of the Lord is the beginning of knowledge: but fools despise wisdom and instruction.

"My son, hear the instruction of thy father, and forsake not the law of thy mother:

"For they shall be an ornament of grace unto thy head, and chains about thy neck." —*Proverbs 1:7–9*

The Mirror of Matsuyama

In Matsuyama there lived a man, his wife, and their little daughter. They loved each other very much, and were very happy together. One day the man came home very sad. He had received a message from the Emperor, which said that he must take a journey to distant Tokyo.

They had no horses, and in those days there were no railroads in Japan. The man knew that he must walk the whole distance,

scarcely: hardly
hover: to fly in the air in one place
reflect: to give back a likeness of something
image: a person or thing that is very much like another
Emperor: the ruler of an empire or group of nations

and that meant that he should have to spend days away from home. He would miss his wife and daughter, and they would miss him.

Still he must obey his Emperor, so he made ready to start. His wife was very sorry that he must go, and yet a little proud, too, for no one else in the village had ever taken so long a journey.

She and the baby walked with him down to the turn in the road. There they stood and watched him through their tears, as he followed the path up through the pines on the mountain side. At last, no larger than a speck, he disappeared behind the hills. Then they went home to await his return.

For three long weeks they waited. Each day they spoke of him, and counted the days until they should see his dear face again. At last the time came. They walked down to the turn in the road to wait for his coming. Upon the mountain side someone was walking toward them. As he came nearer they could see that it was the one for whom they waited.

The good wife could scarcely believe that her husband was indeed safe home again. The baby girl laughed and clapped her hands to see the toys he brought her.

There was a little red monkey of cotton, with a blue head. When she pressed the spring, he ran to the top of the rod. Oh, how wonderful was the next gift! It was a *tombo,* or dragonfly. When she first looked at it she saw only a piece of wood shaped like a "T." The cross piece was painted with different bright colors. But the odd thing, when her father twirled it between his fingers, would rise in the air, dipping and hovering like a real dragonfly.

Last, of course, there was a *ninghio,* or doll, with a sweet face, slanting eyes, and such wonderful hair. Her name was O-Hina-San.

Then the father handed his wife a small white box. "Tell me what you see inside," he said. She opened it and took out something round and bright.

On one side were buds and flowers of frosted silver. The other side at first looked as clear and bright as a pool of water. When she moved it a little, she saw in it a most beautiful woman.

"Oh, what a beautiful picture!" she cried. "It is of a woman, and she seems to be smiling and talking just as I am. She has on a tan dress just like mine, too! How strange!"

Then her husband laughed and said, "That is a mirror. It is yourself you see reflected in it. All the women in Tokyo have them."

The wife was delighted with her present, and she looked at it very often. She liked to see the smiling red lips, the laughing eyes, the beautiful dark hair.

After a while she said to herself: "How foolish this is of me to sit and gaze at myself in this mirror! I am not more beautiful than other women. How much better for me to enjoy others' beauty, and forget my own face. I shall only remember that it must always be happy and smiling or it will make no one else happy. I do not wish any cross or angry look of mine to make anyone sad."

She put the mirror carefully away in its box. Only twice in a year she looked at it. Then it was to see if her face was still such as would make others happy.

The years passed by in their sweet and simple life until the baby had grown to be a big girl. Her *ninghio,* her *tombo,* even the cotton monkey, were put carefully away for her own children.

This girl was the very image of her mother. She was just as sweet and loving, just as kind and helpful.

One day her mother became very ill. Although the girl and her father did all they could for her, she grew worse and worse.

At last she knew that she must die, so she called her daughter to her and said, "My child, I know that I must soon leave you, but I wish to leave something with you. Open this box and see what you find in it."

The girl opened the box and looked for the first time into a mirror. "Oh, Mother dear!" she cried. "I see you here. Not thin and pale as you are now, but happy and smiling, as you have always been."

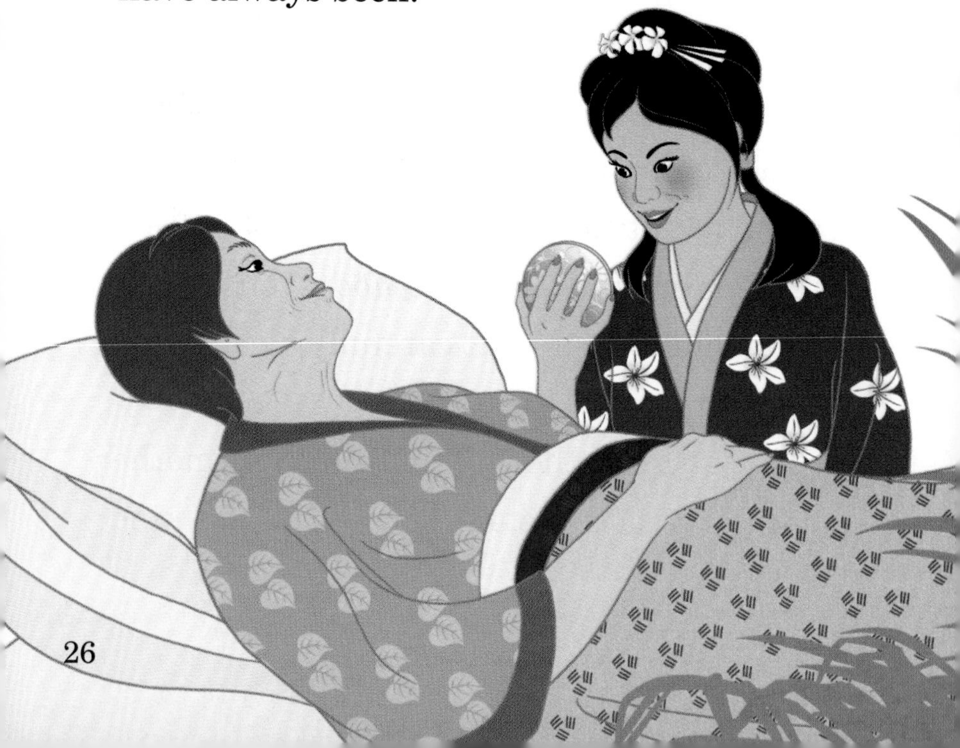

Then her mother said, “When I am gone, will you look in this every morning and every night? Always try to do right, so that you will see only happiness here.”

Every morning when the sun rose and the birds began to twitter and sing, the girl rose and looked in her mirror. There she saw the bright, happy face that reminded her of her mother’s.

Every evening when the shadows fell and the birds were asleep, she looked again. When it had been a happy day, the face smiled back at her. When she was sad, the face looked sad, too. She was very careful not to do anything unkind, for she knew how sad the face would be then.

So each day she grew more kind and loving, and more like the mother whose face she had loved.

Think about it

1. What did the father bring to his child when he returned?
2. What special gift did he give to his wife?
3. Why did she put the mirror away?
4. Who did the daughter think about when she looked into the mirror?
5. What do you think about when you look into a mirror?

The Bible says

"A merry heart maketh a cheerful countenance: but by sorrow of the heart the spirit is broken."

—Proverbs 15:13

Life's Mirror

Give to the world the best that you have,
And the best will come back to you.
Give love, and love to your heart will flow,
And strength in your utmost need.
Have faith, and a score of hearts will show
Their faith in your work and deed.

—Madeline Bridges

Dolly Madison's Brave Act

James Madison of Virginia was the fourth President of the United States. His wife Dorothy was a charming and accomplished woman, beloved by everyone who knew her. She was affectionately known as "Dolly." With her husband she lived for many years in the city of Washington.

In the years from 1812 to 1815, Great Britain made war upon the United States. President Madison had been warned that the

---

accomplished: skilled
beseech: to beg
quantity: an amount
parchment: writing paper made of skins
slender: thin
haste: speed
in vain: without results
canvas: a coarse cloth on which an oil painting is made

British army was about to attack the capital of our country.

Some of the citizens said, "Oh, no; we cannot believe this report; the city cannot be in danger." But very soon they learned that the British forces were coming near, both by water and by land.

It was learned positively that the British commander had boasted that he would capture the city on the very next day, and would eat his dinner in it.

Then there was the greatest excitement. Mounted soldiers galloped along the streets, and they shouted, "The British are marching nearer!"— "The British are pressing forward!"—"The British are coming down the hills!"

Soon Dolly Madison received a message beseeching her to seek at once a place of safety outside the city. But there was something she wished very much to do before going away.

First, she ordered her carriage, and then

she sent away, in a wagon, quantities of rare silver plate and other valuables to be stored in the Bank of Maryland at Baltimore.

In one of the rooms hung a beautiful full-length portrait of General Washington. It was painted by the famous painter, Gilbert Charles Stuart.

"Oh, this picture *must* be saved!" cried Dolly Madison. "The British must not get their hands upon it. I must save it, and I will. But how?"

She moved quickly across the room to the wall on which the picture hung, and with her fingers she tried to loosen the frame from the screws that held it. But the frame was large and heavy, and the screws were firm and fast, and Dolly Madison's fingers were small and slender, and she was in the greatest haste.

She tried in vain to loosen the screws. Finding that she could not do this, she said, "I will save the canvas, even though I have to spoil the frame." Her servants helped her break the frame, and Dolly Madison with her own hands removed the precious portrait from the stretcher. As the canvas fell to the floor, the sound of marching troops was heard.

"Save this picture, save it!" cried Dolly Madison, anxiously, to two of our own soldiers who just then entered the room.

"If you cannot save it, destroy it. It shall never fall into the hands of the British!"

She had now scarcely time to save herself. Snatching up the precious parchment that bore the Declaration of Independence with all its valued signatures, she hastened to her carriage, and was rapidly driven to a place of safety beyond the Potomac River.

The two soldiers carefully rolled up the picture, and it was taken to a farmhouse not many miles away. A few weeks later the famous canvas was restored to Dolly Madison in the White House.

Think about it

1. What caused all of the excitement in Washington, D.C.?
2. What seemed to be most important to Dolly Madison when she learned that the attack was certain?
3. How did Dolly Madison show her love for our country?

I Am Not Bound to Win

I am not bound to win,
But I am bound to be true.
I am not bound to succeed,
But I am bound to live up to what light I have.
I must stand with anybody that stands right;
Stand with him while he is right,
And part with him when he goes wrong.

—*Abraham Lincoln*

One Fourth of July

Grandma had promised the children a Fourth of July story, and Bobby and Alice and Pink drew up their stools and waited eagerly for her to begin.

"Father was going to take us to Clayville to the Fourth of July celebration," Grandma began. "We were all going except Mother and Nanny Dodds, who was helping us over hay harvest. I had been to Clayville once before.

" 'But that time it was on just a common

---

sacrifice: to give up something for someone
earnest: sincere
solemn: serious
pewter: a tin-copper material
lozenge: a small piece of candy
churning: making butter out of cream
surrey: a carriage with a flat top
calico: a cotton cloth with a design
currant: a small berry

everyday day,' as I told Nanny. 'This will be different.'

"We were to start early in the morning, for Clayville was twelve miles away, and we did not want to miss a single thing.

"First there would be a parade with two brass bands, then 'speaking' on the courthouse steps, and after that an ox roast. In the afternoon there were to be horse races and games. Father promised that we should have supper at the hotel and stay for the fireworks in the evening. I had never seen even a firecracker, and I looked forward to seeing the skyrockets most of all.

"I was to wear a new light calico dress with a little blue flower in it and a blue sash and my ruffled white sunbonnet that was kept for Sundays. I talked so much about going that Mother and my sisters and everyone else except Nanny grew dreadfully tired of listening to me and begged me to talk of something else.

"Nanny was twenty and bashful and as

homely as could be, but I loved her very much. When she made cookies, she put a raisin in the center of some of them, and others she sprinkled with sugar. And she made gingerbread men with currant eyes, and baked saucer pies, and let me scrape the cake bowl. She sewed for my doll and bound up my hurt fingers tenderly and told the nicest stories. There was no end to the things Nanny did for me, but I liked the stories best of all.

"The day before the Fourth, when I sat on the edge of the kitchen table watching Nanny beat eggs for the sponge cake and talking about what I should see the next day, Nanny said in a wistful voice, 'I've never been to Clayville. I always thought I'd like to go, but I never had a chance.'

"This set me thinking. Soon I slid off the table and went in search of Mother. I found her at the springhouse churning butter.

" 'Mother,' I said, 'let's take Nanny with us tomorrow.'

" 'I'm afraid there isn't room,' Mother answered regretfully. 'There are already five of you, and the surrey is old and not strong.'

" 'Nanny doesn't weigh much,' I argued.

" 'I know, dear, but Father is afraid to load the surrey any heavier for fear you'd break down and not get to town at all. I have told Nanny she may go home to see her mother tomorrow.'

"All the rest of the morning I sat under the apple tree in the side yard, thinking. When Charlie came through the yard with a jug to fill with water for the men in the hayfield, I called him over. Maybe he might offer to let Nanny go in his place. To be sure, I hadn't much hope of this, but still it was worth trying.

“ ‘Charlie,’ I said, ‘I think Nanny would like to go to the Fourth of July celebration.’

“ ‘Sure, who wouldn’t?’ he replied easily. ‘I want to go myself,’ and he went on to the well.

“I tried sister Belle next. I found her plucking chickens in the orchard and offered to help. Then presently I suggested to her that she could go to Clayville with the Strangs, since their surrey would not be as crowded as ours would, and then Nanny could go with us. She only laughed scornfully, and made me finish plucking the chicken I had started.

“I went sadly back to the apple tree.

“ ‘Nanny wants to go,’ I thought to myself, ‘and I want to go, too, but if I stay at home, Nanny could go in my place. It would be a sacrifice,’ I sighed deeply. ‘Preacher Hill says a sacrifice is giving up something you want yourself. I want to go more than I ever wanted anything, but I have lots of things Nanny doesn’t have. I have curly hair, and Nanny’s hair is straight. I can read, and Nanny can’t.

I've seen the train and had my dinner at a hotel. I've traveled, and Nanny's never been farther from home than Mt. Zion Church.'

"That night after I had said my prayers, I put my arms around my mother's neck and whispered, 'Mother, I want Nanny to go in my place tomorrow.'

" 'Why, dear!' Mother started to protest. But after looking earnestly into my face she said, 'Do you really want to stay at home and let Nanny go in your place? You must be very, very sure, you know.'

" 'I'm sure, Mother,' I declared solemnly. 'Yes, I'm sure I want her to go.'

" 'Well, sleep on it, and if you feel the same in the morning, you shall stay with Mother, and Nanny may go.'

"I wakened at daylight to find Mother standing beside my bed.

" 'Are you awake, Sarah?' she asked. 'They are all up but you.'

"I sat up in bed dazed. I could hear the girls rushing around in their room. From the kitchen came the rattle of dishes, and out in the barn the boys were whistling. Suddenly I remembered, it was the Fourth of July!

" 'I haven't changed my mind, Mother,' I said, yawning sleepily.

"Mother bent down and kissed me before going to tell Nanny. At first Nanny would not hear of it, and left off getting breakfast to come and tell me so. I pretended to be too sleepy to talk, so Nanny, urged by Mother, finally went away to get ready, and Mother went down to finish getting the breakfast.

"But I wasn't a bit sleepy a little later when I jumped out of bed to watch them start.

"Father and Aggie sat on the front seat of the surrey, and Belle, Nanny, and Charlie on the back seat, while Joe, Stanley, and Truman rode horseback. They all looked very fine and grand to me dressed in their best clothes, and I choked back a sob as they drove down the road and out of sight.

"All morning I helped Mother. I did lots of things the girls wouldn't let me do when

they were doing the work. I dried the dishes and fed the chickens and dusted the sitting room and scrubbed the walks.

"Then Mother and I had our lunch out under the apple tree in the side yard—some of everything the girls had put in their lunch basket—fried chicken and sponge cake and green-apple pie. My, but it tasted good! In the afternoon Mother made my doll a new dress, and we went together to hunt the little turkeys and get the cows.

"It was awfully late when the folks got

back, but I sat up in bed to see them. Every one of them had brought me something. Spread out on the bed were a flag and a bag of peanuts, a pewter tea set from Father, a sticky popcorn ball, and sack of peppermint lozenges, but the nicest of all was when Nanny gave me a hug and whispered, 'I had the grandest time of my life, Sarah, and I reckon it'll take me a month to tell you about all the things I saw.'"

Think about it

1. Who was telling this story?
2. What sacrifice did Sarah decide to make?
3. How was she rewarded for her kindness?

The Bible says

"And Jesus answered him, The first of all the commandments is, Hear, O Israel; The Lord our God is one Lord:

"And thou shalt love the Lord thy God with all thy heart, and with all thy soul, and with all thy mind, and with all thy strength: this is the first commandment.

"And the second is like, namely this, Thou shalt love thy neighbor as thyself. There is none other commandment greater than these."

—Mark 12:29–31

The Wallpaper That Talked

Far away in Japan lived little Koto San and her grandmother. As they sat sipping their tea one chilly day, Grandmother said thoughtfully, "My, but I wish I had enough money to buy some wallpaper."

---

foreign: from another country
conscience: a knowledge or sense of right and wrong
continued: kept on
surveyed: looked at
unbelievingly: in an unbelieving manner

"It would be nice to have some pretty new paper!" cried Koto San eagerly. "Please, do try to get some!"

"But we are so poor. We really do need the paper, since it would make the room warmer for the winter, but I'm afraid that I can get nothing with the little bit of money that I have."

Next morning, Grandmother proudly watched Koto San as she skipped to the mission school. Koto San was a bright little girl, and already she could read. Grandmother had wondered if she was doing right when she first allowed Koto San to go to the school of the "foreign devils." But Koto San must have an education, and this was the cheapest way. To soothe her conscience, Grandmother had forbidden Koto San to ever bring home the "foreign devils' terrible book"—the Bible.

Koto San had learned to love the Lord Jesus after hearing about Him from the missionaries, and often she longed to tell Grandmother that the wonderful Lord Jesus loved her, too, and had died for her sins. But because she feared that Grandmother might not allow her to go to the mission school, she kept her secret in her heart and prayed for Grandmother.

After Koto San had gone, Grandmother put on her bright kimono, a long dress with big sleeves and a wide sash. Taking her bit of money, she hurried to the market. What a busy, noisy place! And, oh, what wonderful things there were to buy—if only one had money! At the shops that sold wallpaper, Grandmother was thrilled with the lovely paper she saw, but again and again she shook her head. It was just as she feared. She did not have enough money.

Sadly Grandmother walked slowly homeward. As she passed a neat little house, she noticed its lovely lawn. But what was that lying on the grass? Could it be a box? Had someone dropped it? Grandmother looked up and down the narrow, empty street. Crossing the lawn quickly, she picked up the box, opened it cautiously, and peeked inside.

Oh! Oh! How wonderful! The box was full of paper—paper that had pretty writing marks all over it that meant nothing to

Grandmother, who could not read! The sheets of paper were not large, but there were so many of them that perhaps there would be enough to cover the walls of her room. Once again Grandmother looked up and down the street and at the little house. No one seemed to be watching. Surely the box must have been thrown away. Without waiting any longer, she tucked the box into her big sleeve and hurried home.

Mixing the paste took but a few moments, and when Koto San returned home from the mission school, Grandmother had quite a bit of one wall already papered. "Oh, Grandmother, how nice!" she cried happily. "You did get some pretty paper! I have never seen wallpaper just like this before." Koto San went closer and suddenly she caught her breath. For a moment she looked frightened as she glanced quickly at Grandmother and then back at the paper. Grandmother calmly continued with her work. Koto San's eyes

began to twinkle and sparkle, for Koto San knew something about that paper that Grandmother did not know. Grandmother was pasting the Bible—the "foreign devils' book"—on their walls!

After several days, the room was finished. Grandmother and Koto San surveyed their work proudly. My, but it did look nice! "And to think it didn't cost me anything!" Grandmother was thinking.

"Now I can read the Bible whenever I wish!" Koto San was thinking. After that, as they sat sipping their tea together, Koto San would sit close to the wall so that she could read. Often she wished that she dared to tell Grandmother the secret, but she supposed that Grandmother would tear the paper from the wall if she knew.

One day Koto San thought, "I'll tell her just a little bit to see if she gets angry." "Grandmother, sometimes as I sit here drinking tea, the wallpaper talks to me."

"Talks to you? Why, what nonsense, child." She turned to look at the wall beside her. "Whoever heard of wallpaper talking!"

"But it does!" insisted Koto San.

"Then what does it say if it talks to you?" Grandmother asked unbelievingly.

"Well," began Koto San slowly, "right here it tells how the great God in Heaven made the sun, moon, and stars, and all the wonderful world we live in!" and she read to Grandmother from the first chapter of Genesis.

"How wonderful!" Grandmother exclaimed, hardly able to believe it. "Does it really say that? How strange that I cannot hear it talk," and she bent her ear to the wall. "Does it say anything else?"

"Oh, yes! It tells me how God made and put the first people in the wonderful world, and how He blessed them. But one day they were wicked," and Koto San read the sad story of how sin entered the world when Adam and Eve listened to Satan and disobeyed God by eating of the tree He had forbidden them to eat.

"How sad! Does the wallpaper say whether God punished them?"

"God said they must surely die. If they had not disobeyed, they would have lived forever!"

"Does the wallpaper tell more? Something about that story talks to my heart, for my heart is sometimes wicked. Must God punish me, too?" Grandmother wondered softly. "We must listen again tomorrow and see if it will tell us more."

After that, Grandmother eagerly awaited Koto San's return from school each day. Soon Grandmother learned the good news that God sent His Son into the world to die for all who had sinned against Him. When she heard that God loved her, and that she could accept His Son as her Savior, she trembled for joy! Could these wonderful words be true?

Then one morning after Koto San had gone to school, Grandmother put on her pretty kimono again and hurried down the street. The burden on her heart to know whether this wonderful love story was true or not had grown so great that she had decided she must find out today. Perhaps the people who lived in the house where she had found the box could tell her if the story was true. But would they be angry and think she had stolen it? Grandmother was so anxious to have her questions answered that she went bravely to the little house.

When a foreign woman opened the door, Grandmother could only stare at her green eyes and straw-colored hair. The lady smiled and invited her in. Before Grandmother knew it, she was sitting down pouring out her story. The missionary listened quietly until Grandmother finished; then she got her Bible. As she opened the Book, Grandmother grew more excited. "There it is! Just the

same as my wallpaper! Oh, tell me, please tell me, is it true? Does God really love me?"

With joy in her face the missionary cried, "He does! See here, 'For God so loved the world, that He gave His only begotten Son, that whosoever believeth in Him should not perish, but have everlasting life.' And He says, 'Him that cometh to Me I will in no wise cast out.'"

Before the missionary could say much more, Grandmother was on her knees, weeping her thanks to God for loving a poor old Japanese woman enough to send the Lord Jesus to die for her sins. Then getting to her feet she said, "I am sorry, but I must go now. Thank you, oh, thank you for all you have told me," and she hurried away with a shining face.

When Koto San got home, Grandmother met her at the door. "Oh, Koto San! What do you think I found out today? Our wallpaper is really the Bible!" For a moment Koto San was frightened, but then she noticed the joy on Grandmother's face. "And best of all, Koto San," she hurried on to say, "I found out that it is all true! No one else in all of Japan has wallpaper that talks. Listen, little Koto San, run up and down the street and knock on all our neighbors' doors. Invite the ladies to come to our house for tea and to listen to the wallpaper's good news."

Think about it

1. In what country did Koto San and her grandmother live?
2. What did Grandmother want to buy for their home?
3. Where did Grandmother get the wallpaper?
4. How did the wallpaper "talk" to Koto San?

Can't and Won't

Can't and *Won't* were two sturdy brothers,
Angry and sullen and gruff;
Try and *Will* are dear little sisters,
One scarcely can love them enough.

Can't and *Won't* looked down on their noses,
Their faces were dismal to see;
Try and *Will* are brighter than roses
In June, and as blithe as the bee.

Can't and *Won't* were backward and stubborn,
Little, indeed, did they know;
Try and *Will* learn something new daily,
And seldom are heedless or slow.

Can't and *Won't* loved nothing,—no, nothing
So much as to have their own way;
Try and *Will* give up to their elders,
And try to please others at play.

Can't and *Won't* came to terrible trouble,—
Their story is too sad to tell!
Try and *Will* are now in the schoolroom,
Learning to read and to spell.

---

blithe: (blīth) carefree; merry
dismal: gloomy; dreary
gruff: coarse in voice; rough
scarcely: hardly
stubborn: refusing to obey
sturdy: strong; unyielding
sullen: gloomily angry
terrible: frightful; very bad

Green and Gold

For every leaf of green,
A golden leaf;
For every faded flower,
A yellow sheaf;
For every sunny hour,
A drop of rain;
For every cloudy day,
The stars again.
For every dashing wave,
A pretty shell;
For every sound of woe,
A merry bell;
For every passing care,
A mother's kiss;
And what could better be,
My child, than this?

Becky's Christmas Dream

All alone by the kitchen fire sat little Becky, for everyone else had gone away to keep Christmas and left her to take care of the house. Nobody had thought to give her any presents, or take her to any merry-making. No one had remembered that Christmas should be made a happy time to every child, whether poor or rich.

She was only twelve years old, this little girl from the poorhouse, who was bound to work for the farmer's wife till she was eighteen. She had no father or mother, no friends or home but this, and as she sat alone by the fire, her little heart ached for someone to love and cherish her.

Becky was a shy, quiet child, with a thin face and wistful eyes that always seemed to be trying to find something that she wanted very much. She worked away, day after day,

---

pinafore: a sleeveless apron
cherish: to think highly of
abuse: to hurt by treating badly
idle: not busy
monotonous: doing the same thing over and over
ruddy: red or reddish

so patiently and silently that no one ever guessed what curious thoughts filled the little cropped head, or what a tender child's heart was hidden under the blue checked pinafore.

Tonight she was wishing someone would give her quantities of pretty things, as they did in the delightful children's tales.

"I'm sure I am as poor and lonely as Cinderella, and need help as much as ever she did," said Becky to herself. She sat on her little stool staring at the fire, which didn't burn very well, for she felt too much out of sorts to care whether things looked cheerful or not.

There is an old idea that all creatures can speak for one hour on Christmas Eve. Now, Becky knew nothing of this story, but when she compared herself to Cinderella, and then fell asleep in front of the fire, she was amazed to hear a small voice say,

"Well, my dear, if you want advice, I shall be very glad to give you some, for I've had much experience in this trying world."

Becky stared about her, but all she saw was the old gray cat, blinking at the fire.

"Did you speak, Tabby?" said the child, at last.

"Of course I did. And I have some good advice for you."

Becky laughed at the idea; but Puss, with her silver-gray suit, white handkerchief crossed on her chest, and her kind, old face and cozy purr, did indeed look like a very good Quakerish little grandmother after all.

"Well, ma'am, I'm ready to listen," said Becky respectfully.

"First, my child, what do you want most?" asked Tabby, quite in the style of the old children's story books.

"To be loved by everybody," answered Becky.

"Good!" said the cat. "I'm pleased with that answer, it's sensible, and I'll tell you how to get your wish. Learn to make people love you by loving them."

"I don't know how," sighed Becky.

"No more did I in the beginning," returned Puss. "When I first came here, a shy young kitten, I thought only of keeping out of everybody's way, for I was afraid of everyone. I hid under the barn and only came out when no one was near. I wasn't happy, for I wanted to be petted, but didn't know how to begin. One day I heard Aunt Sally say to the master, 'James, that wild kitten isn't any use at all. You had better drown her and get a nice tame one to amuse the children and clear the house of mice.'

'The poor thing has been abused, I guess, so we will give her another trial and maybe she will come to trust us after a while,' said the good master. I thought over these things as I lay under the barn and resolved to do my best, for I did not want to be drowned. It was hard at first, but I began by coming out when little Jane called me and letting her play with me. Then I ventured into the house, and finding a welcome at my first visit, I went again and took a mouse with me to show that I wasn't idle. No one hurt or frightened me, and soon I was the household pet. For several years I have led a happy life here."

Becky listened eagerly, and when Puss

had ended, she said timidly, "Do you think if I try not to be afraid, but to show that I want to be affectionate, the people will let me and will like it?"

"Very sure. I heard the mistress say you were a good, handy little thing. Do as I did, my dear, and you will find that there is plenty of love in the world."

"I will. Thank you, dear old Puss, for your advice."

Puss came to rub her soft cheek against Becky's hand, and then settled herself in a cozy hunch in Becky's lap. Presently another voice spoke, an odd, monotonous voice, high above her.

"Tick, tick; wish again, little Becky, and I'll tell you how to find your wish."

It was the old moon-faced clock behind the door, which had struck twelve just before Tabby first spoke.

"Dear me," said Becky, "how strange things do seem tonight!" She thought a moment, then said soberly, "I wish I liked my work better. Washing dishes, picking chips, and hemming towels is such tiresome work, I don't see how I can go on doing it for six more years."

"Just what I used to feel," said the clock. "I couldn't bear to think that I had to stand here and do nothing but tick year after year. I flatly said I wouldn't, and I stopped a dozen times a day. Bless me, what a fuss I made until I was put in this corner to stand idle for several months. At first I rejoiced; then I got tired of doing nothing and began to reflect that as I was born a clock, it would be wiser to do my duty and get some satisfaction out of it if I could."

"And so you started going again? Please teach me to be faithful and to love my duty," cried Becky.

"I will"; and the old clock grandly struck the half hour, with a smile on its round face, as it steadily ticked on.

Here the fire blazed up and the teakettle hanging above the fire began to sing.

"How cheerful that is!" said Becky, as the whole kitchen brightened with the ruddy glow. "If I could have a third wish, I'd wish to be as cheerful as the fire."

"Have your wish if you choose, but you must work for it, as I do," cried the fire, as its flames embraced the old kettle till it gurgled with pleasure.

Becky thought she heard an odd voice humming these words:—

"I'm an old black kettle,
With a very crooked nose.
But I can't help being glad
When the jolly fire glows."

"I shouldn't wonder a mite if that child has been up to mischief tonight, rummaged all over the house, eaten herself sick or stolen something and run away with it," fretted Aunt Sally, as the family went jingling home in the big sleigh about one o'clock from the Christmas party.

"Tut, tut, Aunty, I wouldn't think evil of the poor little thing. If I'd had my way she would have gone with us and had a good time. She doesn't look as if she had seen many, and I have a notion it is what she needs," said the farmer kindly.

"The thought of her alone at home has worried me all the evening, but she didn't seem to mind, and I haven't had time to get a respectable dress ready for her to wear, so I let it go," added the farmer's wife, as she cuddled little Jane under the cloaks and shawls, with a regretful memory of Becky knocking at her heart.

"I've got some popcorn and a bouncing big apple for her," said Billy, the red-faced

lad perched up by his father playing drive.

"And I'll give her one of my dolls. She said she never had one, wasn't that dreadful?" put in little Jane, popping out her head like a bird from its nest.

"Better see what she has been doing first," advised Aunt Sally. "If she hasn't done any mischief and has remembered to have the kettle boiling so I can have a cup of hot tea after my ride, and if she has kept the fire up and warmed my slippers, I don't know but I'll give her the red mittens I knit."

They found poor Becky lying on the bare floor, her head pillowed on the stool, and old Tabby in her arms, with a corner of the blue pinafore spread over her. The fire was burning splendidly, the kettle simmering, and in a row upon the hearth stood, not only Aunt Sally's old slippers, but those of master and mistress also, and over a chair hung two little nightgowns warming for the children.

"Well now, who could have been more thoughtful than that!" said Aunt Sally. "Becky shall have those mittens, and I'll knit her two pairs of stockings, that I will."

So Aunt Sally laid the bright mittens close to the little rough hand that had worked so busily all day. Billy set his big red apple and bag of popcorn just where she would see them when she woke. Jane laid the doll in Becky's arms, and Tabby smelled it approv-

ingly, to the children's delight. The farmer had no present ready, but he stroked the little cropped head with a fatherly touch that made Becky smile in her sleep, as he said within himself, "I will do by this forlorn child as I would wish anyone to do by my Janey if she were left alone." But the mother gave the best gift of all, for she stooped down and kissed Becky as only mothers can kiss. The good woman's heart reproached her for neglect of the child who had no mother.

That unusual touch wakened Becky at once, and looking about her with astonished eyes, she saw such wonderful change in all the faces, that she clapped her hands and cried with a happy laugh, "My dream's come true! Oh, my dream's come true!"

The Bible says

"Give, and it shall be given unto you; good measure, pressed down, and shaken together, and running over, shall men give into your bosom. For with the same measure that ye mete withal it shall be measured to you again."

—Luke 6:38

Earning a Violin

"And you don't like to practice!" Grandma exclaimed in surprise when Bobby told her why he did not like to take violin lessons. "But you'll have to practice, you know, or you will never learn to play. I knew a boy once, who dearly liked to practice. I think I'll tell you about him. It was my brother Charlie. Charlie had wanted a violin ever since he was just a little bit of a fellow and had first heard old Mr. Potter play on his violin.

"Mr. Potter was a traveling tailor who went around the country making and mending men's clothing. He carried his goods

---

solemnly: seriously
thriving: successful
ford: to walk or ride across a shallow place in a stream

from place to place in pack saddles, and he always brought his violin along.

"In the evenings he would play, and we all loved to hear him. He played beautifully. All Charlie and I had ever heard before were things like 'Pop Goes the Weasel,' or 'Turkey in the Straw.' There was such a difference between these tunes and what Mr. Potter played that the first time Charlie heard him play—'Annie Laurie,' I think it was—he walked up to him and said very solemnly, 'I like a violin better than a fiddle,' and everybody laughed.

"Years before, Mr. Potter had had a thriving trade, but when I knew him he did not get much to do because store suits for men had become common. Mother always found some work for him, though, and in his spare time he gave violin lessons.

"He was in our neighborhood several weeks each spring, and one winter Charlie determined to have a violin and be ready to take lessons when he came next time.

"So right away he began to save money for a violin. But there wasn't much Charlie could do to earn money, and it looked as though he would never get enough for a violin, let alone enough for an instruction book and lessons. But he did get the violin, and this is how it came about.

"It was one of the coldest winters anyone remembered in years. A deep snow lay on the ground for weeks and weeks, and the roads were frozen hard and as smooth as glass.

"There was a sawmill about eight miles down the road from our house, and every day we could see men passing on their way to the mill with logs. Big iron hooks called 'dogs' would be driven into the logs and fastened to a heavy chain which would be hitched to a horse. It was an easy way to get logs to the mill, and everyone was hurrying to haul as many as possible before the thaw came.

"Father had cut one big walnut log when he had been called to serve on jury duty and had gone to Clayville to attend court. Before he went, Charlie asked him what he would do with that one log, and Father told Charlie he could have it. Charlie could hardly believe his ears, and he asked Father whether he really meant that he could have the money for the log if he could get it to the mill. Father said that was what he meant, but afterward he told Mother he never dreamed Charlie would try to do it.

"But from the first Charlie intended to move that walnut log to the mill. He thought of nothing else. He made plan after plan. He found out from the storekeeper that the man who owned the sawmill came to the store Saturday afternoons to buy supplies for the next week. So when Charlie and I went to the store for Mother on the next Saturday we sat by the stove to warm ourselves and wait for the sawmill man. When he came, Charlie asked him whether he would buy the walnut log.

" 'Well, that depends,' said the man,

looking Charlie over good-naturedly. 'I'm not anxious to lay in any more logs than we've bargained for. We're going to move Wednesday.' Then when he saw the disappointment on Charlie's face he asked, 'Pretty good log, is it?'

" 'Oh, yes, sir,' said Charlie eagerly. 'My father said when he cut it that it was first grade—woods-grown, ten or twelve feet long.'

" 'Well, if that's the case, I reckon I could use it,' said the man. 'Be sure to have it in by Tuesday, though.'

"We went home by way of Mr. Brierly's, and Charlie got permission to borrow his logging chain and 'dogs,' as they were called. We stopped to look at the log, and Charlie declared he could get it to the mill without any trouble. He could have, too, if it hadn't been for the thaw.

"Sunday was the longest day Charlie ever put in. Sometimes he would get discouraged and think he couldn't do it at all. Then the next minute he would be talking about the kind of violin he would get with the money the log would bring. Father had come home for over Sunday, and he would help him get started.

"Sunday, after dinner, the weather turned slightly warmer, and by four o'clock a gentle rain was falling. When Charlie got up long before daylight Monday morning, Mother told him that it had rained hard all night. He fed the horse and ate his breakfast, and Father helped him drive the hooks into the log. Then Charlie was off.

"He got the log as far as Sugar Creek without any trouble, and there what a sight met his eyes! Sugar Creek was out of bank, and the shallow stream, easily forded the year round, was like an angry, rushing little river filled with cakes of ice. To ford it was clearly impossible till the ice went out, and even then the current would be rapid and dangerous. There was nothing to do but wait, and Charlie unhitched the horse and came back home. It was still raining and thawing and it didn't get any better all that day. The next morning, though, the creek was clear of ice, which was some advantage.

"I went with Charlie and sat on the log, feeling very helpless while he walked up and down the creek bank trying to think of some way to get the log across. The current was so strong that, though the horse could swim it, he could not swim and drag the heavy log along.

"Charlie carefully examined the foot log that crossed the creek and found that it had

not been moved by the high water, being chained at each bank to a big tree. Then he made his plan. He fastened some strong rope he had brought along to the chain which went around the walnut log. Holding the other end of the rope, he got on the horse and made him swim to the opposite bank. Then he fastened the rope at that side to the horse's harness and urged the horse up the bank.

"The horse tugged and pulled, and finally the log moved slowly down into the water. Now came the test of Charlie's plan. If the foot log proved strong enough to withstand the jar it would get when the walnut log hit it, everything would be all right; but if the foot log gave way, Charlie would have to cut the rope quickly to keep the horse from being drawn back into the water, and the walnut log would float downstream and be lost.

“I almost held my breath when the walnut log, sucked rapidly down the stream by the swift current, struck the foot log. I shut my eyes tight and did not open them until I heard Charlie shouting for joy. The foot log hadn’t budged! Because of the high water Charlie thought it would be easy for the horse to pull the log out on the ground, but the log stuck on something under the water. Charlie couldn’t raise the log up, and he had to let it slide back into the water. It slid back several times before it finally came out on the road.

“It was nearly noon and Charlie was wet to the waist, so he went back home to change his clothes and get a fresh horse. After dinner he started out again. He got to the mill all right and sold the log, and when he reached home late that night he had money enough for a violin.

"When Father heard about it, he was so proud of him that he doubled the money. So Charlie had more than enough for his lessons and his instruction book, too."

"And did he really like to practice?" asked Bobby unbelievingly.

"Yes, indeed, and he came to be a fine violinist and owned a violin that cost a great deal of money, but he always kept that first one, too."

Think about it

1. Why did everybody laugh when Charlie said, "I like a violin better than a fiddle"?
2. How did men haul logs to the mill? Why were they in a hurry?
3. Why did Father give Charlie the walnut log? Did he think that Charlie could really move it to the mill?
4. What things did Charlie do in order to move the log? Was his job easy? Why was he so determined to get it done?

The Fiery Furnace

Nebuchadnezzar the king made an image of gold, whose height was threescore cubits, and the breadth thereof six cubits.

Then Nebuchadnezzar the king sent to gather the princes, the governors, and the captains, the judges, the treasurers, the counselors, the sheriffs, and all the rulers of the provinces, to come to the dedication of the image.

---

score: twenty
sackbut, psaltery, dulcimer: kinds of musical instruments
cubit: about eighteen inches
image: an idol
astonied: bewildered; astonished

Then all the rulers of the provinces stood before the image that Nebuchadnezzar had set up.

Then a herald cried aloud, “To you it is commanded, O people, nations, and languages, that at what time ye hear the sound of the cornet, flute, harp, sackbut, psaltery, dulcimer, and all kinds of music, ye fall down and worship the golden image that Nebuchadnezzar the king hath set up.

“And whoso falleth not down and worshipeth shall the same hour be cast into the midst of a burning fiery furnace.”

Therefore at that time, when all the people heard the sound of the music, all the people fell down and worshiped the golden image that Nebuchadnezzar the king had set up.

Wherefore at that time certain Chaldeans came near, and accused the Jews.

They said to King Nebuchadnezzar, “O king, live for ever. Thou, O king, hast made a decree, that every man that shall hear the music shall fall down and worship the golden image: and whoso falleth not down and worshipeth, that he should be cast into the midst of a burning fiery furnace.

"Shadrach, Meshach, and Abednego, O king, have not regarded thee: they serve not thy gods, nor worship the golden image which thou hast set up."

Then Nebuchadnezzar in his rage and fury commanded to bring Shadrach, Meshach, and Abednego.

Nebuchadnezzar said unto them, "Is it true, O Shadrach, Meshach, and Abednego, do not ye serve my gods, nor worship the golden image which I have set up? Now if ye be ready that at what time ye hear the sound of the music, ye fall down and worship the image which I have made; well: but if ye worship not, ye shall be cast the same hour into the midst of a burning fiery furnace; and who is that God that shall deliver you out of my hands?"

Shadrach, Meshach, and Abednego answered and said to the king, "O Nebuchadnezzar, we are not careful to answer thee in this matter. If it be so, our God whom we serve is able to deliver us from the burning fiery furnace, and He will deliver us out of thine hand, O king.

“But if not, be it known unto thee, O king, that we will not serve thy gods, nor worship the golden image which thou hast set up.”

Then was Nebuchadnezzar full of fury. Therefore he spake, and commanded that they should heat the furnace seven times more than it was wont to be heated. And he commanded the most mighty men that were in his army to bind Shadrach, Meshach, and Adednego, and to cast them into the burning fiery furnace.

Then these men were bound and were cast into the midst of the burning fiery furnace.

Therefore, because the king’s commandment was urgent, and the furnace exceeding hot, the flame of the fire slew those men that took up Shadrach, Meshach, and Abednego.

And these three men, Shadrach, Meshach, and Abednego, fell down bound into the midst of the burning fiery furnace.

Then Nebuchadnezzar the king was astonied, and rose up in haste, and said unto his counselors, “Did not we cast three men bound into the midst of the fire?”

They answered and said unto the king, “True, O king.”

He answered and said, “Lo, I see four men loose, walking in the midst of the fire, and they have no hurt; and the form of the fourth is like the Son of God.”

Then Nebuchadnezzar came near to the mouth of the burning fiery furnace, and said,

"Shadrach, Meshach, and Abednego, ye servants of the most high God, come forth, and come hither."

Then Shadrach, Meshach, and Abednego came forth out of the midst of the fire.

And the princes, governors, and captains, and the king's counselors saw these men, upon whose body the fire had no power.

Then Nebuchadnezzar said, "Blessed be the God of Shadrach, Meshach, and Abednego, who hath sent His angel, and delivered His servants that trusted in Him, and have changed the king's word, and yielded their bodies, that they might not serve nor worship any god, except their own God." —*from Daniel 3:1–28*

Think about it

1. Can you figure out how tall the image of gold was?
2. Why did Shadrach, Meshach, and Abednego refuse to bow down to the golden image? Do you think they were right? Why?
3. How did God reward the three men for their bravery and obedience?
4. Did Nebuchadnezzar learn something about God because the three men stood true? What did he learn?

The God Who Made Chaluba's Hands

Chaluba watched with pleasure as the thin shavings of wood curled away from his knife. Surely this would be the best god he had ever made. He had been carving idols ever since he was old enough to hold a knife in his hand, but never before had he made one with such a fierce expression on its face. Chaluba smiled as he carved the thin lines for the eyes, the mouth, and the hands.

Suddenly, Chaluba stopped carving. "I am making this god's hands," he thought. "I wonder who made my hands? Surely it

---

despair: to give up hope
approach: to come near to
determine: to decide

was not this idol that I am carving. Why, I have the power to make him or to destroy him. The God Who Made My Hands must be much greater than this idol, for my hands can do many things. But who is He, I wonder? I have never heard the people in the village speak of Him, not even the witch doctor."

Chaluba laid aside his knife and sat thinking. If only he knew more about the God Who Made His Hands!

Soon, the people of the village began talking about Chaluba. "Have you heard?" they said. "Chaluba is not carving idols any more, and he refuses to worship the village gods. The gods will be angry, and something terrible will happen to us."

Finally, the news reached the ears of the witch doctor himself, and he called Chaluba before him. "What is this I hear," he said, "that you not only refuse to do your work, but you also have stopped worshiping our gods? Is it true?"

Chaluba bowed low before the witch doctor, and then he stood straight and tall. "Oh, sir, it is true," he said. "I can no longer worship gods that I have the power to make or to destroy. I want to worship the God Who Made My Hands. But who is He? Can you tell me about Him?"

The witch doctor and the town leaders rose in anger against Chaluba. "The gods will punish us if we allow someone in our village to talk like that," they shouted. "We must kill this boy."

Chaluba ran for his life through the village, across a field, and deep into the jungle. Finally, when he was sure that he was no longer being followed, he dropped, panting, beneath a large tree.

"Now, what shall I do?" he wondered. "I cannot go back to the village—the people would surely kill me. I know! I shall look for the God Who Made My Hands. Who knows? Perhaps I shall find Him."

Chaluba climbed high up into the tree.

It was dark now, and he needed to protect himself from wild animals.

Far off in the jungle, a lion roared, and another answered. "The God Who Made My Hands must have made the lions, too," Chaluba thought, "and this tree, and everything that is in the jungle. I wonder what He thinks of the things He has made? Does He love them and take care of them?"

With this thought, Chaluba fell asleep. He awoke early the next morning and determined to begin his search.

Chaluba wandered from village to village, always asking, "Have you seen the God Who Made My Hands? Can you tell me about Him?"

Always, the frightened people shouted,

"The gods will be angry!" And Chaluba had to run for his life.

At last, someone told Chaluba of a very old and very wise man named Mamba. Mamba had gone to the government post years ago, and had returned to his village with a magic that made marks on wood and paper talk.

"Perhaps this wise man can tell me what I want to know," Chaluba thought. He went to Mamba's village, found the hut where he lived, and told him his story. "And you, who are so wise," Chaluba said, "can you tell me about the God Who Made My Hands? I do want to know Him!"

Mamba was so old that his voice trembled as he replied, "My son," he said, "many years ago I went down the river to the government post and learned to read, for that is the magic of marks on wood and paper. While I was there, I heard someone speak of a Book which tells of a God who made the jungle and all that is in it. I have never seen that Book myself, but if you stay here with me, I will teach you to read, and then maybe you can find the Book for yourself."

Chaluba did stay with Mamba for days, weeks, and months. He studied hard each day, and finally he knew the magic of reading. After he had been with Mamba for about a year, Mamba died, and Chaluba was left alone.

"Now, what shall I do?" he thought. "I know! I shall go down the river to the government post and find the God Who Made My Hands."

Chaluba made himself a canoe and began

the long, lonely trip down the river. He paddled for days and days, and at last he saw the buildings of the government post. Would he find the answer to his question here?

With fear in his heart, Chaluba approached the strange white man who stood in the doorway of one of the buildings. "Please, sir," he said, "I am looking for the God Who Made My Hands. Does He live here?"

The white man only laughed. "Go back to your village," he said gruffly. "There is no room for you here."

In despair, Chaluba paddled back up the river to his village. Before he entered the

village, he fell to his knees. "Oh, God Who Made My Hands," he cried, "I have tried and tried to find you, but always I fail. If you want me to know You, You must show Yourself to me."

To earn a living, Chaluba became a hunter. Sometimes he would be gone for many days looking for meat for the people of the village. As he returned from one such trip, the people ran to meet him.

"Oh, Chaluba," they cried. "What you have missed while you were gone! The very day that you left, a strange man came to the village with a box of black Books. He spoke to us of a God who made the jungle and all that is within it, and who loves the things that He made, and. . . . But wait! When we told him about you and your magic of reading, he left one of the Books for you. It is on the platform in the center of the village."

Chaluba trembled as he approached the center of the village. Could this be his answer at last? He stepped onto the platform and reached for the Book.

With shaking hands, he opened it to the first page and read:

"In the beginning God created the Heaven and the earth."

Could this Book really be about the God Who Made His Hands? On and on Chaluba read, not stopping even to eat.

"No man hath seen God at any time; the only begotten Son . . . hath declared him."

"For God so loved the world, that he gave his only begotten Son, that whosoever believeth in him should not perish, but have everlasting life."

At last, Chaluba closed the Book. Falling to his knees, he cried out, "Oh, God Who Made My Hands, I do believe that. I believe that You made me and that You love me. I believe that You sent Your Son to die for my sins. At last, I have found You! I have found the God Who Made My Hands."

Think about it

1. Where do you think Chaluba lived? What things in the story showed you this?
2. How did Chaluba know that the idols could not be real?
3. Why were the people in the villages angry with Chaluba?
4. Why did the people think that reading was magic?
5. Chaluba asked God to show Himself to him. Did God answer that prayer? How did He do it?

The Bible says

"And ye shall seek me, and find me, when ye shall search for me with all your heart."

—*Jeremiah 29:13*

Bergetta's Misfortunes

Old Bergetta lay asleep on the doorstep in the sun. Bergetta was a cat of an inquiring mind. Now, an inquiring mind is a very good thing if it is not too largely developed, but Bergetta was just a little bit too curious.

This morning, she was having a beautiful nap in the spring sunshine. Her two little white forepaws were gathered in under her chin, and she had encircled herself with her tail in the most compact and comfortable

---

extraordinary: not usual
hideous: horrible; very ugly
bristling: stiff with fear
vise: a small tool used to hold things tightly
observe: to notice or watch
uttered: spoke
mingled: mixed
awe: fear, wonder
dismay: fear
merciless: cruel
console: to comfort

way. Now and then she lifted her sleepy lids and winked a little, and perhaps she saw, or did not see, the bright blue ocean at the end of the rocky slope before her, and the white sails here and there, and the white clouds dreaming in the fresh and tender sky of spring.

Presently, a sound broke the stillness, and she pricked up her pretty pink-lined ears and listened intently. Two men, bearing a large basket between them, came in sight, approaching the house from the beach. The basket seemed heavy; the men each held a handle of it, and carried it to the back entrance of the house.

Bergetta settled her head once more upon her folded paws and tried to go to sleep again. But the thought of the basket prevented her

What could be inside that basket?

She got up, stretched herself, and lightly and noiselessly made her way around the house to the back door and went in. The basket stood in the middle of the floor, and the three other cats sat at a respectful distance from it, surveying it doubtfully.

Bergetta wasn't afraid. She went slowly toward it to investigate its contents. When she was quite close to it, she became aware of a curious noise going on inside—a rustling, crunching, dull, clashing sound. She stopped and listened; all the other cats listened. Suddenly, an odd object thrust itself up over the edge, and a most extraordinary shape began to rise gradually into sight. Two long, dark, slender feelers waved about aimlessly in the air for a moment. Two clumsy claws grasped the rim of the basket, and by their help a hideous, dark body, bristling with points and knobs, and cased in hard, strong,

jointed armor, with eight legs flying in all directions rose before the eyes of the astonished cats. Each leg was fringed at the foot with short, yellowish hair, and the inner edges of the huge claws were lined with a row of sharp, uneven teeth, opening and shutting with the grasp of a vise.

It was a living lobster.

Those among you who never have seen a living lobster would be quite as astonished as the cats were at its unpleasant appearance. It seems a mixture of spider and dragon. Its jet-black, shining eyes are set on short stalks and project from its head, and the round balls turn about on their stems and survey the world with a hideous lack of feeling.

It has a long jointed tail, which it claps together with a loud clash, and with which it draws itself backward with wonderful rapidity.

Such was the hard and horny monster that raised itself out of the basket and fell with a loud noise all in a heap on the floor before Bergetta. She drew back in alarm, and then sat down at a safe distance to observe this strange creature. The other cats also sat down to watch, farther off than Bergetta, but quite as much interested.

For a long time all was still. The lobster, probably rather shocked by its fall, lay just where it had landed. Inside the basket, a faint stirring and wrestling and clashing was heard from the other lobsters—that was all. Bergetta crept a little nearer the basket.

"I needn't be afraid of that thing," thought she. "It doesn't move any more."

Nearer and nearer she crept, the other cats watching her, but not stirring. At last she reached the lobster which sat blowing a cloud of rainbow bubbles from its mouth but making no other movement. Bergetta ventured to put out her paw and touch its hard shell. It took no notice of this, though it saw Bergetta with its odd eyes on stilts.

She tried another little pat. The lobster waved its long antennae, or feelers, that streamed away over its back in the air.

That was charming! Bergetta was delighted. The monster was really playful! She gave him another little pat with her soft paw, and then boxed his ears, or the place where his ears ought to be. This was fun! First with the right and then with the left paw, she gave him little cuffs and pushes and pats which moved him no more than a rock. At last he seemed to become suddenly aware of Bergetta's presence, and he began to move his huge front paws uneasily.

Still Bergetta frisked about him, till he thrust out his eight smaller claws with a gesture of displeasure, and opened and shut the clumsy teeth of the larger ones in a way that was quite dreadful to behold. "This is *very* funny," thought Bergetta. "I wonder what it means!" and she pushed her little white paw directly between the teeth of the larger claw which was opening and shutting slowly. Instantly, the two sides snapped together with a tremendous grip, and

Bergetta uttered a scream of pain. Her paw was caught as in a vise.

In vain she tried to get away; the lobster's claw clasped her delicate paw in a grasp altogether too close for comfort. Crying with fear and distress, Bergetta danced about the room, and everywhere Bergetta danced, the lobster was sure to go, too, clinging for dear life. Up and down, over and across, they went, in the wildest kind of jig, while all the other cats made themselves as small as they could in the remotest corners and watched the performance with mingled awe and dismay. At last, someone heard the noise and came to the rescue, thrusting a stick between the clumsy teeth and loosening the grip of the merciless claw. Poor Bergetta, set at liberty, limped off to console herself as best she might.

For days she went limping about, so lame she could hardly creep around the house. When at last she began to feel a little better, she strayed one day into the same room, and seeing a pan of milk on the table, jumped up on the table to investigate. Naughty Bergetta! She did not wait for anybody's permission, but straightway thrust her pink nose into the smooth, creamy surface.

Now, it was washing day, and just under the edge of the table, on the floor behind Bergetta, was a tubful of hot suds. She lifted up her head after her first taste of the cream. Oh, horror, what did she see? Just opposite her on the table was another lobster with its long feelers bristling. It had been boiled, by the way, but of course Bergetta could not know this.

She gave one terrified leap backwards and fell, splash! into the tub of warm suds.

What a commotion! With eyes, ears, nose, and mouth full of soapy foam, she crawled out of it and ran to the door and out into the cold, leaving a long stream of suds behind her. The wind blew through her soaked fur and chilled the marrow of her bones.

Poor Bergetta! All the other cats came

round her and stared at her with astonishment, and I'm afraid if cats ever do laugh, they certainly laughed at Bergetta when she told them her morning's experience.

I don't think she ever teased a lobster again or tried to steal milk from the pan, but she went mewing about, rubbing her cheek against the kind little cook's foot till she gave her all a cat could wish.

And let us hope that she escaped any more such dire disasters during the rest of her life.

Peggy and the British General

During our war for freedom the British captured a thousand of our men at the battle of Camden, in South Carolina. Among the prisoners was a young captain named Joshua White.

The news made Captain White's family very unhappy. There were five children, and the mother was sick in bed.

Peggy, the oldest child, was fifteen. She was a fearless little patriot. She dearly loved her father. She liked to hear of his brave fighting under the gallant General Sumter.

Now all was changed. Some friend brought word that her father was starving in the prison at Camden. The young girl was greatly excited.

---

gallant: stately; brave and noble
sentinel: someone set to guard a group

"Father is not going to starve, if I can help it," she declared, in her girlish wrath. "I am going to ride over to Camden and see about it."

"No, no, Peggy," replied her mother; "it is thirty-five miles, and the roads are full of British soldiers. I cannot let you go."

"But, Mother," said Peggy, "Father must not go hungry. I will go straight to Lord Cornwallis. I know he will let me carry food to Father."

"No, dear child, you would never get a chance to speak to so great a man as Lord Cornwallis. He would never bother to see a young girl like you. Let us wait awhile. Your father may escape. I am sure he would never want you to risk your life in this way."

"Well, Mother, could I do this? Could I ride on Kitty, my saddle horse, and take old Pompey with me? He can ride on one of the work horses and carry a basket of food."

At last her mother consented.

Before sunrise the next day Peggy and

Pompey, an old servant, started off on their ride to the camp of Lord Cornwallis. By taking short cuts through the woods and hiding when straggling soldiers passed by, they traveled safely all day.

Late in the afternoon they came in sight of the British general's headquarters.

"Please, sir, I wish to speak to General Cornwallis," Peggy said to the guard.

"No," said the sentinel; "you cannot see him. This is no place for you. His lordship is too busy to talk with you. So run along home."

Peggy was not a bit afraid of the tall sentinel.

"But, sir," she said, "I have come on horseback a long way to see the general. I must see him for a moment. Please let me pass."

The guard lost his temper and spoke harshly to her.

Lord Cornwallis was sitting in his room making plans for the war. The loud talking of the sentinel at the porch disturbed him.

"Go and find out what that talk is about," he said to one of his officers; "I wish to be quiet."

"Your lordship," said the officer, on his return, "it is a young girl with an old servant, and she says she must speak to you."

"Let the young miss come in."

No doubt Peggy's courage failed her, and she blushed and began to stammer when she took her first look at the famous man. How fine he must have seemed in his scarlet uniform with its lace and gold buttons!

But the general treated his guest with great kindness.

"Don't be afraid, little miss; there is nobody to do you any harm. I have a little girl of my own in England. What can I do for you?"

"Oh, sir, my poor father is in prison, at Camden, and is awfully hungry. I have brought some goodies for him in this basket. Please may I carry it to him?"

In a few minutes Peggy had told Lord Cornwallis the whole story of her long ride, of her father at Camden, of her sick mother, and of the four little children at home.

The British general listened to her simple but pathetic words. His heart was touched.

He patted her on the head, and taking her by the hand, said, "Dear little girl, you may carry the food to your father this evening, and tomorrow he may go home with you."

We do not know how Peggy was able to thank Lord Cornwallis for his kindness.

Of course there was a joyful time at the plantation when Peggy, Father, and old Pompey came home.

Captain White was so proud of his brave little daughter that he had a pair of gold earrings made for her by the village locksmith.

Peggy lived many years. In her old age nothing pleased her more than to show her

homemade earrings to her grandchildren and tell them of her long ride and of her call on Lord Cornwallis.

Think about it

1. What war was going on when this story takes place?
2. What report did the family receive about Captain White?
3. What was Peggy determined to do?
4. Who did Peggy take with her to Camden?
5. Why do you think Lord Cornwallis helped Peggy?

General Lee

"Robert is both son and daughter to me," Mrs. Lee used to say of her young son.

She was a widow and an invalid, and he was her nurse and mainstay. Leaving the other boys at play, every day he hurried home from school. With gentle, loving hands he assisted her to the carriage, and then sitting by her side cared for and entertained her.

"Unless you are cheerful," he would remind her, "the drive will not do you good."

Robert Lee loved fun and frolic as well as any boy, and was first on the playground. He was first in the schoolroom, too, and there he was always faithful and diligent.

If he had to draw on his slate a figure which was to be erased the next minute, he did it carefully. Whatever is worth doing at all, he thought, is worth doing well.

His father had been a famous soldier, and Robert, too, wished to enter the army. So he went to West Point to learn to be a

soldier. He studied there four years, and in all that time he did not receive one mark for bad conduct.

It was years after he left West Point before he had much fighting to do. At last there was a war between Mexico and the United States. Captain Robert Lee went with the army to Mexico.

Just before a battle, he rode out with a Mexican guide to learn the position of the enemy's army. Mile after mile he went beyond the American lines. At last he saw what appeared to be the enemy's tents showing white in the moonlight. Even then he would not turn back, but rode on to get within earshot.

And lo! the supposed army proved to be a flock of sheep. The drovers gave him the news he wished, and he galloped back to camp.

Another time he was sent out to explore the country. He had a road made across the rough ground, and he guided the soldiers over it. Then at night, alone, in the rain, he went back to the general to report and to give his plan of attack.

No wonder the general said that Robert Lee was the greatest soldier in America.

Captain Lee fought for the United States and loved it. Only one thing was dearer to him—his native state. It was a sad day for him when she left the Union. He was offered command of the Union army, but he refused it. He must live or die with Virginia.

So he gave up his command in the United States army and took command of the Virginia forces. Afterward he was made commander in chief of the Confederate army.

He led his men to victory after victory. They loved "Marse Robert," as they called him, and were willing to run any risk if he were safe.

In one battle he placed himself at the head of some men from Texas. “My Texas boys, you must charge,” he said. “Hurrah for Texas!”

But up and down the line went the shout, “Go back, General Lee, go back.”

A gray-haired soldier seized his bridle and said, “General Lee, if you do not go back, we will not go forward.”

So General Lee went back, and the brave Texans dashed on to victory and death.

The Confederate soldiers lacked food, clothing, and supplies of every kind. There was, in fact, only one thing which they did not lack—that was the soldier’s brave spirit.

General Lee shared the hardships of his men. When his friends sent him food, he gave it to his wounded soldiers or sick prisoners, and he himself ate no more than his men did.

Now, there was one great difference

between the army of the North and that of the South. Whenever a man in the northern army was killed, another soldier took his place. But when a southern man fell, it left a gap in the ranks. Even the old men and boys were already in the field, and the Confederacy had no money to hire foreign troops.

The little army of ragged, starved, unconquered men grew smaller and smaller. At last General Lee saw that to hold out longer would be a useless waste of life. "I would rather die a thousand deaths than surrender," he said; yet that was what he must do.

He looked sadly at the noble soldiers who had faced death in so many battles.

"Men, we have fought the war together," he said. "I have done the best I could for you."

The South admired General Lee in both victory and defeat. Even those who had fought against him respected him—the great general, the Christian gentleman.

After the war he was poor and homeless. People who admired him offered him money as gifts or salary, but he refused all.

He determined to devote the remainder of his life to the education of southern boys. And so he became president of Washington College, now Washington and Lee University. There he died at his post of duty.

Stealing a Cannon Ball

When I was thirteen years old, my father moved from a country town to the city of Boston. The thing that impressed me most about the area was its ships.

The navy yard in Charleston, across the Charles River, was my special wonder and glory. I became familiar with all its marvels. I crept down to the bottom of the huge unused ships; I climbed up to the decks of

---

desire: a wish
possess: to own
construction: building
dry dock: a dock used for building and repairing ships
vault: an underground storage room
shinny: field hockey, played with sticks and balls

those that were being built in the covered shiphouses; I watched the construction of the famous dry dock; I ranged along the silent mouths of the awful cannons.

One day I visited some vaults where cannons had been stored. The six- and twelve-pound balls were extremely tempting. I had no special use for them. I am to this day puzzled to know why I desired them. There was no chance to roll them in the house or in the street. For baseball or shinny they were too large and heavy.

But I was seized with a strong desire to possess one. As I had been well brought up, of course my first objection was that it would be stealing. I disposed of that on the plea that it was no sin to steal from the government.

Next, how should I carry the ball from the yard without being caught? I tried it in my handkerchief. That was altogether too plain. I tried my jacket pocket, but the sag and shape of that aroused my fears. I tried my pants pocket, but the big lump was worst of all. I had a good mind to be honest, since there was no satisfactory way of stealing the ball. At length a thought struck me—wrap a handkerchief about it and put it in your hat.

I quickly wrapped the ball in my handkerchief, mounted it on my head, and shut the hat over it. I came out of the vault a little less courageous than was pleasant, and began my march toward the gate. Every step seemed a mile; every man I met looked unusually hard at me. The sailors evidently suspected my hat. Some mariners strolling toward the ships seemed to look me through. The perspiration stood out over my face as an officer came toward me. Now for it! I was to be arrested, beaten, or shot, for all I knew. I wished the ball were at the bottom of the sea; but no, it was on top of my head.

By this time, too, it had grown very heavy. I must have made a mistake in selecting it. I meant to take a six-pounder and before I got out of the yard, it weighed twenty-four pounds. I began to fear that the stiffness with which I carried my neck would excite suspicion; and so I tried to limber up a little, which really ruined me, for the ball rolled around on my crown in a manner which nearly brought me and my hat to the ground. Indeed, I felt like a loaded cannon, and every man and everything was like a spark, trying to touch me off. The gate was much farther away than I had ever found it before. I seemed likely never to get there.

When, at length, heartsore and headsore, with my scalp well rolled, I got to the gate, all my terror reached its height as the guard stopped his marching, drew himself up, and looking at me, smiled. I expected him to say, "Oh, you thief, you little imp! Do you think that I do not see through you?" But, bless his heart, he only said, "Pass." He did not say it twice. I walked a few steps farther, and then, having great faith in the bravery of my feet, I pulled my hat off, and, carrying it before me, I whipped around the first corner and made for the bridge with the speed of a race horse.

When I reached home, I had nothing to do with my cannon ball. I dared not show it in the house or tell where I got it, and I gave it away the same day.

But after all, that six-pounder rolled a good deal of sense into my skull. It was the last thing I ever stole, and it taught me the foolishness of wanting more than one can enjoy.

Think about it

1. Was the boy right when he said that it was no sin to steal from the government?
2. Why did he think that the ball now weighed twenty-four pounds?
3. Instead of giving the ball away, what should the boy have done with it?
4. What lesson did the boy learn though his experience?

The Bible says

"Let him that stole steal no more: but rather let him labour, working with his hands the thing which is good, that he may have to give to him that needeth."

—Ephesians 4:28